Warren Community Elementary

W9-CKJ-902

WARREN COMM. ELEM SCHOOL
51 SCHOOLHOUSE DRIVE
WEST WARREN, MA 01092-0446

BUMPÉ

christopher carlson

illustrations by bengt lindberg

skaniimal press

love and thanks to mom, lara, and guy

skaniimal press published by skandiiplaay ltd

skandiiplaay 743 alexander road bldg 15 princeton NJ 08540

first published in the united states of america in 1998 by skaniimal press,
a division of skandiiplaay, ltd

text © 1998 by christopher e carlson illustrations © 1998 by bengt lindberg

this book is published under exclusive license from bengt lindberg and stefan saidac,
the owners of the bumpé character and the trademark bumpé

all rights reserved

without limiting the rights under copyright reserved above, no part of
this publication may be reproduced, stored in or introduced into a retrieval system,
or transmitted, in any form or by any means
(electronic, mechanical, photocopying, recording or otherwise),
without the prior written permission
of both the copyright owner and
the above publisher of this book.

isbn 0 9667826 0 7

printed in hong kong

library of congress catalog card number 98-90917

book conceptual design by christopher carlson

to caryn brooks,
bumpé's muse

bumpé's from Scandinavia
a far north habitat-
he lives among the skaniimals
and wears an elaborate hat

I must say this
that bumpé thinks
and starts to change
in stages-
slowly but surely
he turns into things
his little thought
engages

a

bumpé thinks of
airplanes
his arms flap
up and down
soon he makes
propeller noises
high above
the ground

b

bees and bumpés
both take flight
a buzzing bumpé bumble-
but how they fly
is a riddle-
aerodynamically
they should tumble

C

sometimes bumpé's
little form
produces
cappuccino
steam comes out
his yellow ball
whistling
like a
Puccini
concertino

d

in jurassic times
the **dinosaurs**
roamed
towering above
your head-
the question is
were bumpésaurs
there
and were they
green instead ?

e

which came
first
the bumpé
or
the **egg-**
who
can really say ?
was he
hatched
or already there
or designed
by
Fabergé ?

f

if you scattered
bumpé seeds
and wished
for **flowers**
to tend
bumpé poppies
soon would bloom
lowing
in the wind

g

a **gadget** is
a kind of a
gizmo
a specialized
mechanical thing-
a thingamabob
for a bumpé-
a widget
that winds
bumpé's spring

h

balloons are filled
with **helium**
a gas that's
lighter than air-
let's fill bumpé up
with this
and tie off
his *derriére*

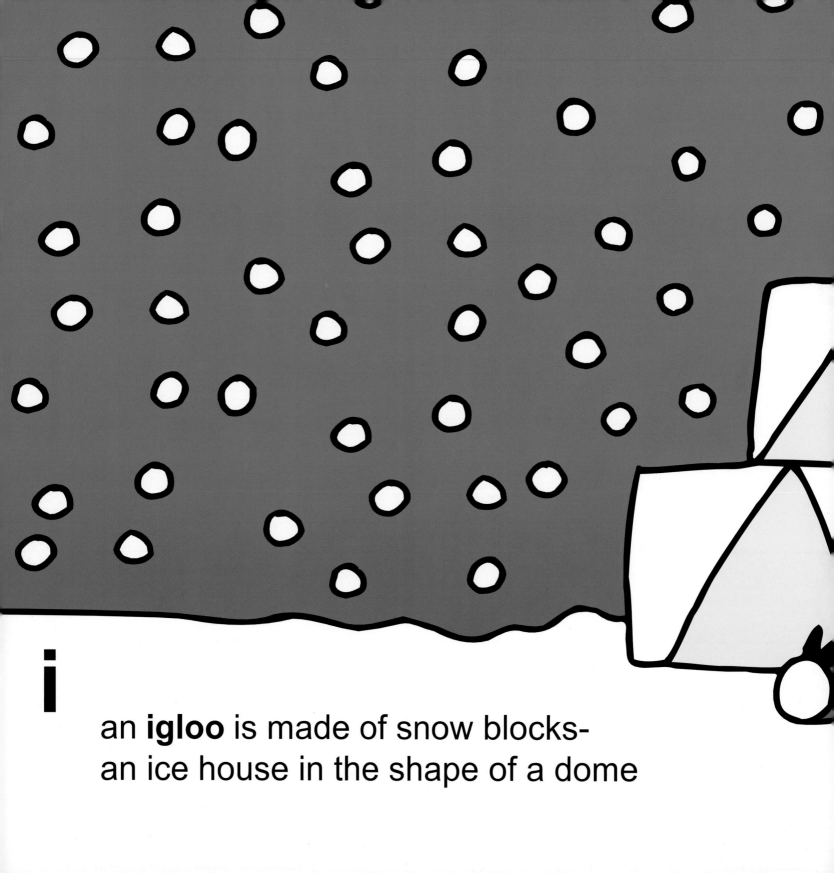

i

an **igloo** is made of snow blocks-
an ice house in the shape of a dome

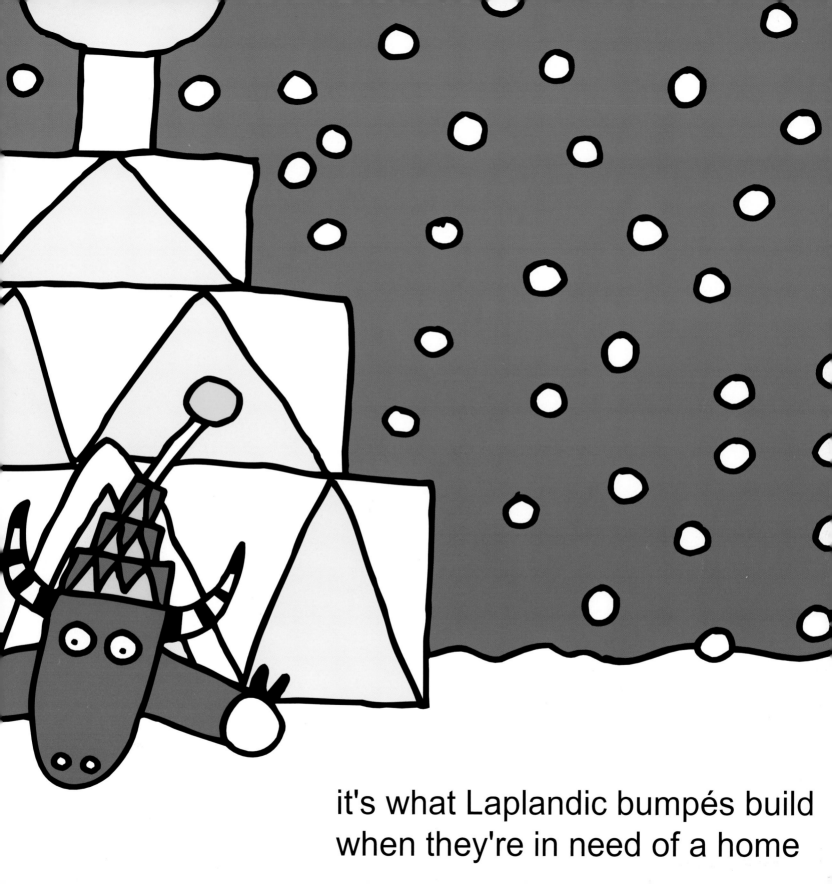

it's what Laplandic bumpés build
when they're in need of a home

j

bumpé blues
jazz quartet-
four Blue Notes
begin their set

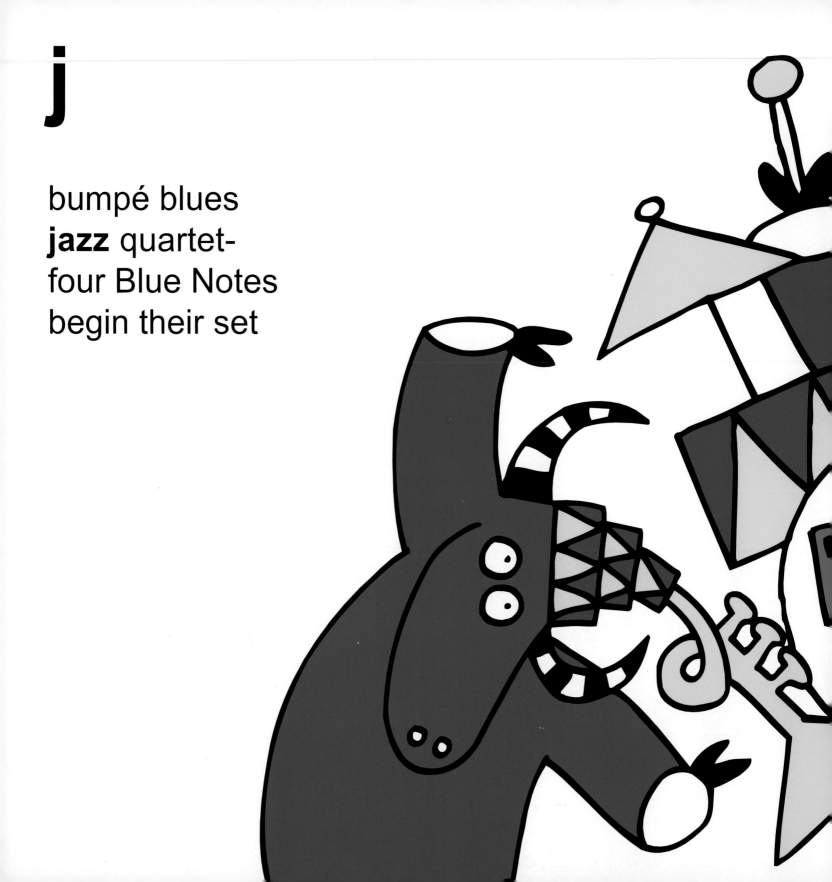

k

bumpé has a
string attached
a strong wind
starts to blow-
a billowing bumpé
sails aloft-
a **kite** with
striped tail
and
red bow

l

a **lobster** is
a crustacean
with claws that
look like
maracas-
they dance the
rhumba in a
conga line
with bumpé in
sea shell
pajamas

m

the **maltese** bumpé
is a mystery
from the start-
can you find
this little red
statue
before
Humphrey Bogart ?

n

a **note** is
a musical letter
grouped
to form a
song

let's replace
all the notes
with bumpés
and have
a sing-along

o

an **opera** is
a musical drama
that's over when
the fat lady
sings-
there's a kind called
bumpé buffa-
comic opera
where
the bovine's
the thing

p

Egypt's ancient **pyramids** contain stories in hieroglyphic- the reign of Pharoah Bumpé-Ra the theme most prolific

q

if you open
an atom
there are
smaller **quarks**
within-
smaller still
are a
billion bumpés
dancing on the
head of a
pin

r

bumpé is a
radio
with
a yellow ball
antenna-
change the
stations
with his horns-
from pop to
classical's
Three Tenors

S a **seal** has flippers
and swims the sea
a ball balanced on its nose-

it looks a lot like bumpé does
wearing rubber clothes

t

a **tree** falls
in the forest
does it make
a sound ?
does bumpé
keep on mooing
when you're
not around ?

u

unicorns are mythological horses- and in gardens do reside- they have one horn in the middle of them and bumpés have one on either side

V

bumpé bumpé
quite contrary
how does your
garden grow ?
can you name
these **vegetables**
lined up
in a row ?

W

words are used
upon a page
to tell the thoughts
we think-
write them down
with bumpé's ball
dipped
in india ink

X

x is used to
mark the spot
you're standing on
right now-
you are here
and bumpé's there-
wherefore art thou,
cow ?

y

yoga involves meditation
and bending into positions-
bumpé can easily adapt
to these philosophical conditions

z

bumpés graze
savanna grass
'midst **zebras**
on the veldt,
trekking the
plains of
the Serengeti,
to the oasis
of the Sahara's
Tafilelt

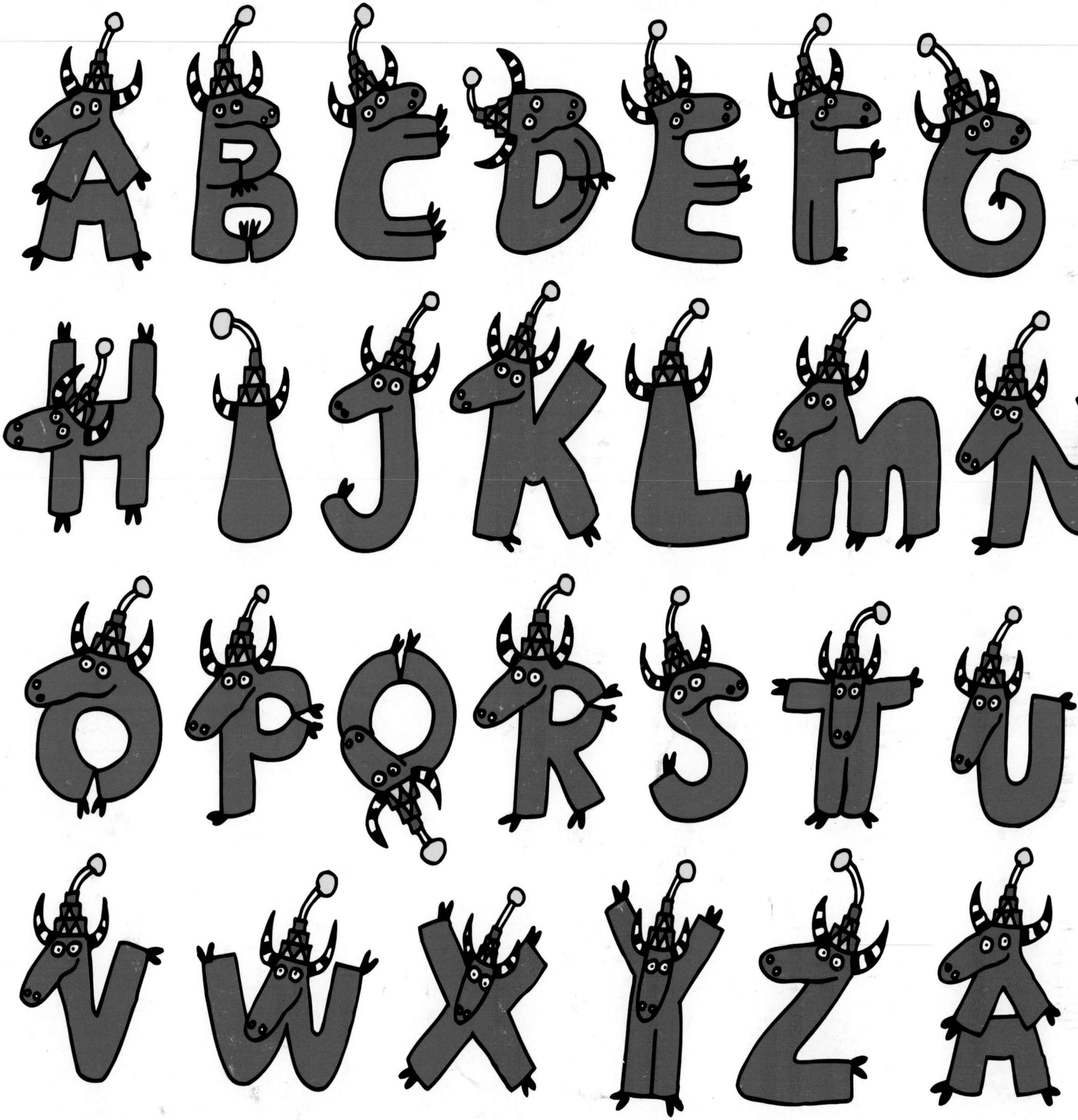
ABCDEFG
HIJKLMN
OPQRSTU
VWXYZA